Author: Terry Paquet Illustrator: Mike Polito Designer: Alisa Baldwin Editor: Isabel Fonte

INSTRUCTIONS:
Beaver Ed's Beaver Tales is the silliest, funniest, happiest, craziest, most awesome word game you'll ever play.

Just follow these simple directions:
Before every story in this book, you'll find four columns of words, each marked with a symbol. Each symbol represents the following:

Symbol

NOUN

VERB

ADJECTIVE

WACKY WORDS

In each story, you'll find blank spaces marked with any one of the symbols above. Fill in each blank space with a word from that column until all the blank spaces in the story are filled. Finally, read your Beaver Tales aloud to see what kind of wacky, silly, hilarious story you've created.

Change the words and you'll have a different story every time!

3

REVIEW

Just so you know:

A NOUN  **is the name of a person, place or thing.**
Teacher, park, ear, and bus are **nouns.**

A VERB  **is an action word.**
Fly, run, throw, and bite are **verbs.**

An ADJECTIVE  **describes something or somebody.**
Fat, tall, cute, round, and thick are **adjectives.**

A WACKY WORD **is any word that will make the story wackier.**

My Favourite City

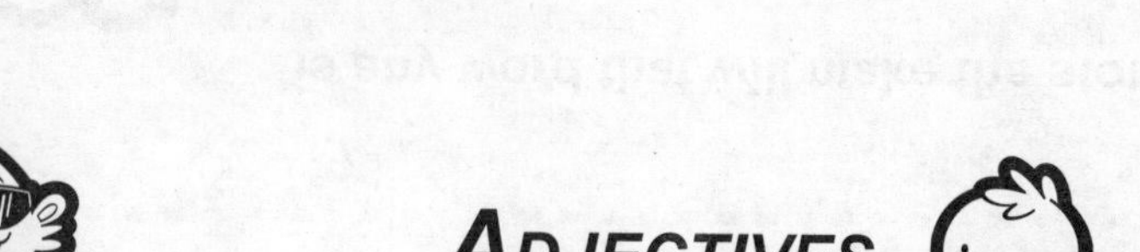

Hey kids...use the words on this page or make up your own words for each story.

Nouns

Slugs
Pugs
Cockroaches
Flies
Beagles
Cowboys
Clowns
Toupées
Jugglers
Worms
Beetles
Noses

Adjectives

Dumb
Fat
Lazy
Ugly
Bald
Stinky
Steamy
Rotten
Putrid
Skinny
Pink
Dirty

Verbs

Squirm
Vomit
Spin
Ache
Shake
Burn
Rattle
Cry
Sing
Swing
Tumble
Explode

Wacky Words

Flickadelphia
Boreeda
Calisnorya
Torunto
Winneslug
Vanpoover
Poorus
Pickleville
Boogerland
Pimple-onia
Noo Zork
Watawa

My Favourite City

Of all the cities in the world, my favourite has to be Pimple-onia. A great little place that is home to 325,791 slugs. All of them are pink flies in disguise, but you wouldn't know that if you saw them. They are so Dirty, they love to make visitors Rattle at the airport by offering them a big, Dumb glass of blended noses. That's their way of saying "welcome." The emblem on the city flag features two Juggler holding a/an Fat flower. The national dish is made of Lazy beans grown in Flickadelphia. One spoonful of this spicy, ugly concoction and your insides will Ache for days.

The Family Reunion

Hey kids...use the words on this page or make up your own words for each story.

NOUNS

Aliens
Meatballs
Clowns
Pigs
Gargoyles
Pimples
Boogers
Warts
Gangsters
Teachers
Donkeys
Monkeys

ADJECTIVES

Stupid
Scary
Nasty
Purple
Gigantic
Smelly
Spooky
Mini
Unhappy
Tasteless
Hairy
Miniature

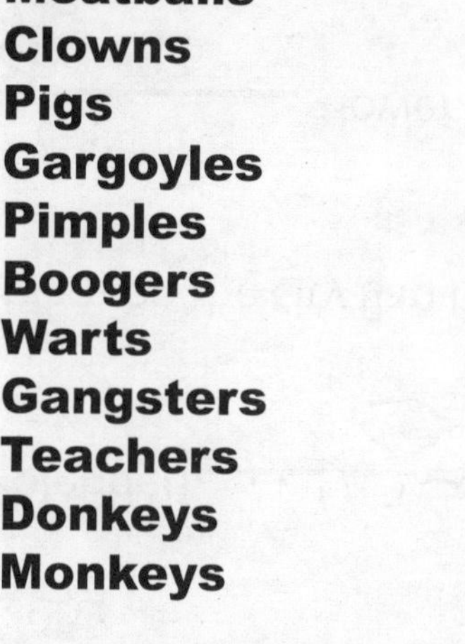

VERBS

Scratch
Itch
Burp
Snooze
Holler
Belch
Tinkle
Bowl
Wiggle
Complain
Vomit
Shave

WACKY WORDS

Picklenose
Spotface
Runnynose
Bigbutt
Beeblebum
Horseshoe
Yellowteeth
Kissyface
Puckerlips
Jigglebelly
Bugeyes
Flemm

The Family Reunion

Today, for the first time ever, we are having a very ____________ family reunion. 125 ____________ have been invited and every one of them said they would ____________ . The whole ____________ clan will be there. We are going to have a/an ____________ meal at a/an ____________ Italian restaurant called Mama ____________ , the best place in town to ____________ and ____________ . I can't wait to reconnect with my favourite ____________ including my ____________ Uncle Morty ____________ , my ____________ Aunt Sally ____________ and even my first cousin, Billy ____________ , king of the ____________ .

It'll be a great opportunity to ____________ , make some ____________ memories and be with the ones I love.

Breakfast of Champions

Hey kids...use the words on this page or make up your own words for each story.

NOUNS

Plumbers
Accountants
Fire fighters
Ballerinas
Hobos
Jugglers
Beekeepers
Oysters
Babysitters
Bank robbers
Nerds
Geeks

ADJECTIVES

Dirty
Smelly
Oily
Soiled
Greasy
Mouldy
Stupid
Horrible
Wicked
Awful
Silly
Ridiculous

VERBS

Dance
Spit
Shake
Shiver
Jump
Scream
Run
Sing
Whisper
Sleep
Snore
Whistle

WACKY WORDS

Knishy
Knoshy
Knashee
Flardy
Furty
Hamook
Karky
Willby
Groosh
Papoopa
Liggy
Diggy

Breakfast of Champions

4 out of 5 ________________ agree that breakfast is the most important meal of the day. In my house, it's a/an ________________ time to fuel up, ________________ and get the energy you need to ________________ until night falls. Studies have shown that ________________ who skip breakfast are more likely to eat ________________ meals at lunch. Some people think a muffin and a hot cup of ________________ is a great way to start the day off, but I know you need to eat something with more nutritional value like fresh ________________ , a slice of ________________ ________________ or toasted ________________ . Other great ideas would be boiled ________________ or baked ________________ with a big glass of ________________ orange juice.

Pet Store

Hey kids...use the words on this page or make up your own words for each story.

Nouns

Mouse
Lion
Doberman
Bunny
Parrot
Elephant
Giraffe
Dolphin
Chihuahua
Bee
Duck
Pony

Adjectives

Slimy
Rubbery
Rotten
Stupid
Mouldy
Hairy
Pink
Musty
Smelly
Gross
Boring
Crunchy

Verbs

Gallop
Fly
Hop
Trot
Swim
Climb
Whistle
Jog
Dance
Crawl
Shoot
Eat

Wacky Words

Meow
Woof
Sssss
Bawk
Beep
Zzzzz
Pffft
Ring
Chirp
Tweet
Moo
Vroom

Pet Store

As soon as I stepped into ________________ Pete's Pet Emporium, I knew it was different. The first animal I saw was a ________________ ________________ sitting on a perch at the front door. It took one look at me and let out a loud ________________. I wanted to ________________ but a ________________ ________________ in a ________________ box grabbed me and pushed me away from the door. It let out a high-pitched ________________ and started to ________________ like a ________________ ________________. Was this some kind of ________________ dream? Every ________________ in every ________________ cage was going nuts, so I asked the salesperson what was wrong? You know what she said? ________________!

How to Brush Your Teeth

Hey kids...use the words on this page or make up your own words for each story.

Nouns

Warts
Boogers
Earwax
Stew
Hairballs
Broccoli
Toenails
Pimples
Gum
Icing
Paint
Cement

Adjectives

Stinky
Fat
Large
Wobbly
Horrible
Disgusting
Crazy
Boring
Jumpy
Itchy
Sweaty
Wacky

Verbs

Spit
Mangle
Twist
Flatten
Squeeze
Spew
Mash
Lick
Chew
Squash
Crush
Boil

Wacky Words

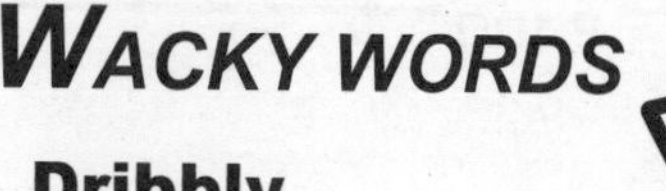

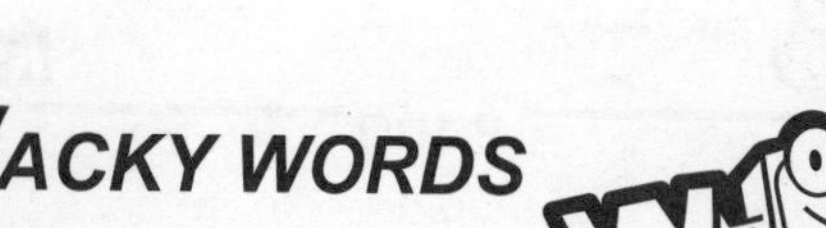

Dribbly
Mentle
Dilly
Wonky
Dootle
Ratty
Toothy
Slurpy
Mushymouth
Bucky
Rottenish
Gooey

WORDPLAY 3

How to Brush Your Teeth

__________ some __________ onto a/an __________ toothbrush. Make sure it contains __________ and has the __________ Dental Association seal. Use __________, circular motions to clean the outside surfaces of your __________. Follow that with gentle brushing to clean the inside surfaces of the front teeth . Remember to clean carefully along the __________ gum line. This is extremely important, as __________ disease starts here. Brush gently because you don't want to __________ your gums. Make sure to brush your back molars where __________ like to hide. Spit out the __________ and rinse your mouth with __________ or mouthwash. Try to floss at least once a day, since most cases of __________ __________ occur between teeth.

Hockey

Hey kids...use the words on this page or make up your own words for each story.

NOUNS

Grannies
Kittens
Butterflies
Hamsters
Kittens
Armpits
Diapers
Meatballs
Mothballs
Eyebrows
Underwear
Chimps

ADJECTIVES

Fake
Boring
Dull
Stupid
Slimy
Devious
Sneaky
Shifty
Greasy
Smelly
Deranged
Angry

VERBS

Booed
Howled
Yawned
Cried
Juggled
Jiggled
Gargled
Burped
Choked
Cackled
Wiggled
Wept

WACKY WORDS

Bobo
Shorty
Burpanbelch
Curlyhead
Stubbynose
Puckface
Fatty
Twinky
Beadyeye
Blubberbutt
Sabre-tooth
Picklehead

Hockey

Of all the players in the National ________________ hockey league, ________________

Madison is truly the best. He played left wing for the Mighty ________________

his entire career. His best game ever was against the ________________

________________ in 1998 when he scored three ________________ goals

on ________________ Le BadBreath, the number one goalie in the whole

________________ league. That night the crowd ________________ and

________________ for three straight periods. They were so ________________

they threw ________________ on the ice. The ________________ referee,

Sammy ________________, ________________ when he realized he would

have to stop the ________________ game and clean the ice all by himself.

What a job!

Turtle

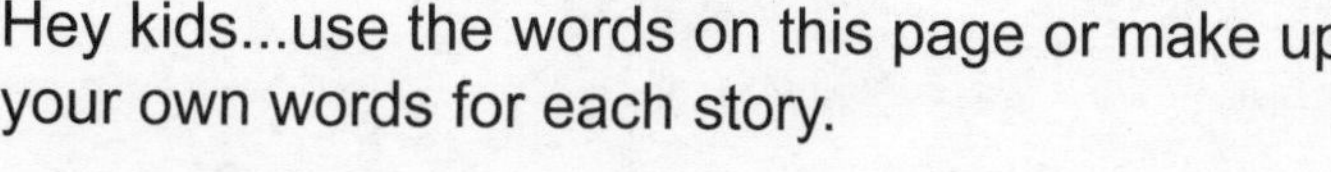

Hey kids...use the words on this page or make up your own words for each story.

Nouns

Banana
UFO
Blender
Oven
Ambulance
Shoebox
Motorcycle
Pizza
Toilet
Kiwi
Dandelion
Meteor

Adjectives

Yellow
Stinky
Skinny
Teeny
Lemony
Round
Shiny
Vile
Sleepy
Happy
Angry
Grumpy

Verbs

Waltz
Jiggle
Drive
Sneeze
Disco
Beep
Crawl
Jump
Sing
Read
Skate
Moonwalk

Wacky Words

Clonk
Boogerstein
Peepoo
Cranky
Jiggerson
Piggo
Buggeyes
Wonkyface
Bobbreath
Nosee
Clunky
Sturper

Turtle

____________ Butt, my pet turtle, isn't like other animals in the neighbourhood.

For starters, he has a/an ____________ shell that looks like a/an ____________.

Every time we go for a walk, ____________ people always stop and point.

But that's not the half of it. My neighbours, Mr. and Mrs. ____________, have

been complaining for years about his ____________ smell. They used to think

it was a/an ____________. Once, they got so ____________, they had

to call for a/an ____________. When my mom found out, she got so

____________ she put the turtle in a/an ____________ for a whole

week. The poor thing, he wasn't allowed to ____________ or

____________ for days.

My Description

Hey kids...use the words on this page or make up your own words for each story.

NOUNS

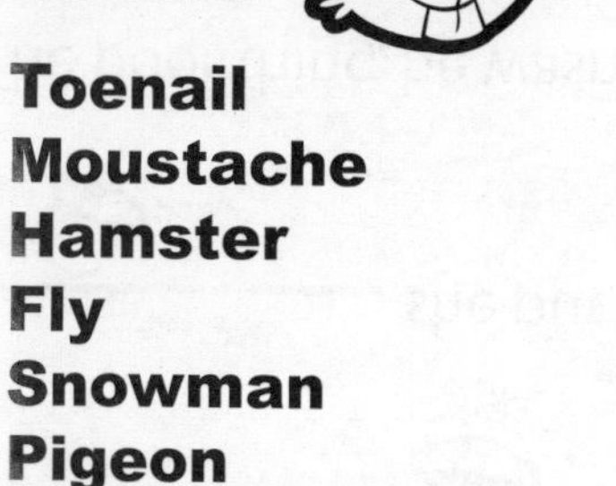

Toenail
Moustache
Hamster
Fly
Snowman
Pigeon
Tree
Finger
Chihuahua
Tomato
Hospital
Airport

ADJECTIVES

Ugly
Horrific
Stupid
Idiotic
Crusty
Weird
Purple
Funny
Damp
Stunning
Dirty
Chubby

VERBS

Flip
Spin
Burp
Jiggle
Shave
Bark
Wiggle
Scratch
Yodel
Scream
Fly
Boil

WACKY WORDS

Beanface
Doofus
Ding Dong
Atchoo
Weezer
Geezer
Dogbreath
Noodlebrain
Noogie
Bigbelly
Nobrain
Fisheyes

My Description

Since you don't really know me, I think I should describe myself. That way, if we ever ________________ one day, you'll recognize my ________________ face. My name is ________________ Johnson but my ________________ friends call me ________________. I have ________________ hair and a small ________________ on my left cheek. My eyes are ________________ just like my dad's. If I ________________ too much, my ________________ turns red. I weigh as much as a/an ________________ and I am as tall as a/an ________________. People say I look like the famous movie star, ________________ Jones but I know they're only being ________________.

Beaver's Ed's Top 10 Songs

Hey kids...use the words on this page or make up your own words for each story.

NOUNS

Rat
Fork
Nose
Ogre
Bean
Meatball
Hair
Diaper
Pig
Yo-yo
Beard
Mosquito

ADJECTIVES

Clumsy
Nutty
Pink
Short
Ugly
Jolly
Toasty
Spotty
Itchy
Squiggly
Nosy
Nasty

VERBS

Burp
Bark
Chew
Wink
Scratch
Bite
Scream
Push
Punch
Paint
Choke
Drool

WACKY WORDS

Bluebeard
Nosehair
Pygmy
Dumbbrain
DingDong
Nerdynut
Yahoo
WaWa
Pimpleface
Beanbag
Butterface
Wirehair

Beaver's Ed's Top 10 Songs

1. You ain't nothing but a ________________ by Elvis ________________.
2. Every little ________________ you take is magic by The ________________ Pigs.
3. Wake me up before you go ________________ by ________________ Michaels.
4. Girls just wanna have ________________ by ________________ Looper.
5. I just want to be your ________________ by ________________ Picklebreath.
6. He ain't heavy he's my ________________ by The ________________ club.
7. Sometimes when we ________________ by ________________ ________________.
8. I just called to say I ________________ you by Stewie ________________.
9. Have you ever really loved a/an ________________ by ________________ Adams.
10. I left my ________________ in San Francisco by Tony ________________.

5 Nursery Rhymes Gone Wrong

Hey kids...use the words on this page or make up your own words for each story.

NOUNS

Bum
Brain
Toenail
Sardine
Tree
Candy
Money
Mountain
Pickle
Wig
Kumquat
Chihuahua

ADJECTIVES

Horrible
Dumb
Smelly
Bad
Dreary
Freaky
Toxic
Wacky
Pink
Childish
Foolish
Wicked

VERBS

Fly
Squish
Burp
Bump
Stab
Bust
Kiss
Scratch
Jump
Eat
Beat
Swim

WACKY WORDS

Bungling
Flippling
Mangling
Farpling
Quertying
Burpaling
Scrampling
Whiffling
Nibbling
Trumbling
Puddling
Dribbling

5 Nursery Rhymes Gone Wrong

#1 Jack and Jill went up the ________________ to ________________ a pail of ________________ (s). Jack fell down and broke his ________________ and Jill came ________________ after

#2 Humpty Dumpty sat on a/an ________________. Humpty Dumpty had a ________________ ________________. All the King's ________________ (s) and all the King's ________________ (s) couldn't put Humpty together again.

#3 Jack be ________________ ,Jack be ________________. Jack jumped over a ________________.

#4 Baa, baa, black ________________ , have you any ________________?

Yes sir, yes sir, three ________________ s full.

#5 Peter Peter ________________ eater, had a ________________ but couldn't ________________ her. He put her in a ________________ shell and there he kept her very well.

Things to do Today

Hey kids...use the words on this page or make up your own words for each story.

NOUNS

Rat
Cockroach
Sewer
Monkey
Toothbrush
Tow truck
Diaper
Girdle
Underwear
Cauliflower
Bicycle
Computer

ADJECTIVES

Ugly
Striped
Ratty
Mouldy
Rusty
Pretty
Pointy
Dirty
Pink
Hairy
Tasty
Zany

VERBS

Change
Jolt
Scare
Cook
Paint
Peel
Shock
Clean
Bounce
Scrape
Scratch
Kick

WACKY WORDS

Gerbilface
Slobby
Badbreath
Flabbygut
Figgy Doo
Jumpy
Yellowteeth
Hairynose
Nelephant
Noodlelegs
Spittle
Giggles

Things to do Today

- Pick up Talia's ________________ at dry cleaner's.

- ________________ Mary for soccer practice.

- ________________ the ________________ car.

- Call Dr. ________________ and make appointment.

- Speak to Uncle ________________ about a/an ________________ ________________.

- Meet Miss ________________ to book a/an ________________ lunch next week.

- Clean out the ________________ and get an extra ________________ to ________________.

- ________________ Cole's ________________ teacher about the field trip.

- Get ________________ for ________________ party on the weekend.

- Book a/ an ________________ treatment at the ________________ spa.

- Write a/an ________________ thank-you letter to Principal ________________.

Pool Rules

Hey kids...use the words on this page or make up your own words for each story.

NOUNS

Gerbils
Dumbbells
Elephants
Avocados
Bricks
Sharks
Goldfish
Kittens
Diapers
Raisins
Marshmallows
Lampshades

ADJECTIVES

Heavy
Orange
Grumpy
Gold
Happy
Fat
Sharp
Blue
Rare
Old
Broken
Rusty

VERBS

Shake
Swim
Breathe
Dance
Talk
Burp
Drool
Scratch
Smile
Live
Kiss
Sing

WACKY WORDS

Flinkalonia
Flartadelphia
Flootyville
Clumsy Land
Mouldy avenue
Roach-o-rama
Doghouse lane
Villa Mushface
Mustachio lake
Wawaville
Kissy-Poo projects
Pimple City

Pool Rules

1. It is forbidden to ________________ in the pool area.

2. ________________ are to be used in case of emergency.

3. ________________ ________________ must be worn in the deep end at all times.

4. Visitors may ________________ and ________________ in the ________________ section only.

5. Minors are not allowed to ________________ unless accompanied by two ________________.

6. Make sure the ________________ are locked when you leave the pool.

7. This pool is only for residents of ________________. All other visitors must show two valid ________________.

8. Remove all ________________ ________________ when not in use.

9. This pool has a capacity of 32 ________________.

Rules for Babysitters

Hey kids...use the words on this page or make up your own words for each story.

NOUNS

Teachers
Plumbers
Toilets
Pigs
Mascots
Dwarves
Electricians
Unicorns
Fairies
Feet
Robots
Giraffes

ADJECTIVES

Stinky
Sticky
Fatty
Skinny
Hairy
Bony
Burnt
Furry
Bushy
Shaggy
Soggy
Muscular

VERBS

Burp
Eat
Spank
Choke
Jiggle
Wash
Drink
Chew
Scratch
Snore
Cook
Boil

WACKY WORDS

Florping
Wibbling
Crinking
Blagging
Croobing
Turbing
Snigging
Snoobling
Wabbling
Winking
Zinzinning
Quorbing

Rules for Babysitters

1. Do not let ________________ in the ________________ house for any reason.

2. Keep all ________________ locked outside.

3. Remember to place all ________________ out of reach of the children.

4. Do not let children ________________ the ________________ without asking the parents first.

5. When you feed the ________________, make sure the food is ________________ .

6. Keep the children away from ________________ ________________ at all times.

7. Remove all ________________ ________________ from the crib before you let the child ________________ .

8. ________________ the cat will not be tolerated under any circumstances.

9. Make sure all ________________ children do not put ____________ ____________ in the electrical outlets.

6 Headlines in Today's Paper

Hey kids...use the words on this page or make up your own words for each story.

NOUNS

Burger
Ferret
Horseshoe
Dwarf
Booger
Hare
Iguana
Unicorn
Teacher
Owl
Princess
Spoon

ADJECTIVES

Giant
Tiny
Illegal
Evil
Thin
Bald
Boring
Terrible
Dreadful
Stinky
Crazy
Flabby

VERBS

Shake
Chop
Cook
Ignore
Cure
Aggravate
Boil
Burn
Lick
Decorate
Fight
Bake

WACKY WORDS

Bugeyes
Blondboy
Fibblelips
Dribbledrops
Weepants
Nevernose
Baggyshorts
ChickenLegs
FloppyCheeks
Whicky Doo
Pawpaw
Quackity Quack

6 Headlines In Today's Paper

1. Man chases __________ __________ with pointy __________ .

One __________ pedestrian injured.

2. Mayor __________ declares next Tuesday National __________ day.

3. Studies show one __________ in 10 will __________ Canadians for

__________ purposes.

4. Ping Pong legend Jimmy __________ denies wrongdoing in missing

__________ case.

5. This weekend's biggest movie, Attack of the __________ __________,

number one at the box office.

6. President __________ to address citizens on major __________

shortage.

The Weather Report

Hey kids...use the words on this page or make up your own words for each story.

NOUNS

Boulder
Clown
Garbage
Hair
Sweat
Puke
Hamster
Flea
Weasel
Ladybug
Gum
Toupee

ADJECTIVES

Hairy
Stinky
Rotten
Polluted
Greasy
Soupy
Green
Dirty
Squishy
Stupid
Flabby
Dumb

VERBS

Singing
Eating
Dancing
Burping
Kissing
Flying
Yodelling
Wiggling
Snorting
Digging
Roasting
Eating

WACKY WORDS

Nosehair
Gunk
Fatty
Locust
Pinky
Bug
Kitty
Munky
Chunky
Buttface
Gassy
Sock

The Weather Report

Hi, I'm ________________ Johnson, your ________________ meteorologist, here with your ________________ weather forecast for the day. This morning, we're looking at ________________ skies with intermittent periods of ________________ showers in the city. This afternoon, we expect Tropical Storm ________________ to move in, bringing huge amounts of ________________ (s) to the area so prepare to do some ________________. That ________________ weather system will be ________________ all the way to the coastal areas and change into a small ________________ by midnight. Tomorrow, don't forget your umbrellas because we're looking at mainly ________________ skies with ________________ patches in the morning and the possibility of a major ________________ storm in the afternoon!

A Message from our Sponsor

Hey kids...use the words on this page or make up your own words for each story.

NOUNS

- Baseball cap
- Monkey
- Banana
- Gargoyle
- Troll
- Wig
- Cabbage
- Clown
- Plunger
- Pig
- Tricycle
- Gerbil

ADJECTIVES

- Plastic
- Wacky
- Pretty
- Strange
- Stinky
- Slimy
- Chubby
- Bloated
- Grimy
- Soiled
- Revolutionary
- Rotten

VERBS

- Juggle
- Curse
- Grunt
- Sneeze
- Wiggle
- Burp
- Fly
- Giggle
- Breathe
- Chew
- Barf
- Draw

WACKY WORDS

- Winky
- Wanky
- Clicky
- Dum Dum
- DinkyDip
- Doody
- Zlotky
- Wacka Wacka
- Whizzz
- Smick
- Shoopy
- Muzzlemouth

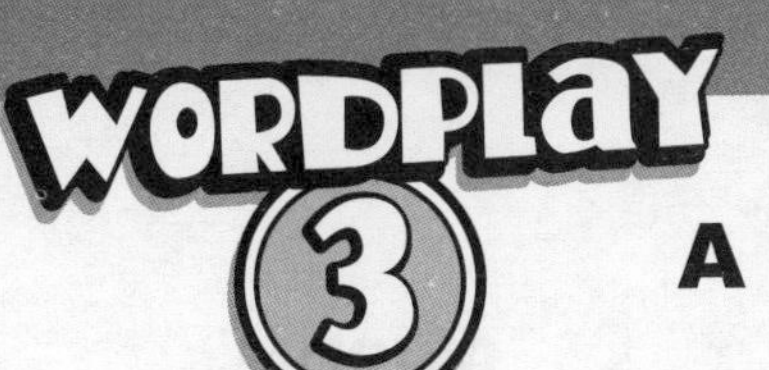

A Message from our Sponsor

Hey kids! Do you have trouble trying to ______________ at night? Does your head feel like a ______________ ______________ after a long day at school? Do your friends say you look like a ______________ ______________? If so, it's time for Uncle Walter's ______________ ______________ cream.

A ______________ product that will change the way you ______________ for the rest of your ______________ life. Call now and we'll throw in one ______________ ______________ for free! But that's not all! Be the first ______________ to order, and we'll also give you a truckload of ______________ ointment to share with your favourite ______________. It's new! It's now!

It's really ______________.

The Big Apple

Hey kids...use the words on this page or make up your own words for each story.

NOUNS

Leprechauns
Monkeys
Pigeons
Babysitters
Clowns
Baboons
Fairies
Dwarves
Pigs
Caterpillars
Bees
Plumbers

ADJECTIVES

Slimy
Goofy
Weird
Ugly
Dizzy
Wild
Dumb
Stupid
Hairy
Outrageous
Insane
Tired

VERBS

Shriek
Sing
Howl
Burp
Squeal
Growl
Sneeze
Dance
Decorate
Snore
Wash
Stomp

WACKY WORDS

Blubberty
Bing Bong
Rubbernose
Polka dot
Diggy Doo
Wipple Wonk
Fishybreath
TurtleHair
Pigpookle
Spittleface
Plimpire
PurpleTeeth

The Big Apple

This is my first trip to New York City and I'm feeling a little ______________ .

After all, I have heard all the ______________ stories about giant ______________

living in the sewers. I even saw a news report about a pack of ______________

______________ lurking in the alleys. But that won't stop me. This is, after

all, home to some of the nicest ______________ this side of ______________

county. That's why I'm determined to see the world famous Statue of ______________

and the ______________ in Central Park that ______________ day and night.

I won't leave without tasting the legendary snack, ______________

______________ on a stick. Yum!

Check out many more great
Beaver Tales *from Beaver Ed!*

Go to **www.beaverbooks.ca**

Colour Beaver Ed!

Test your trivia with **Beaver Ed's Brain Busters**™, another fun game by Beaver Books!

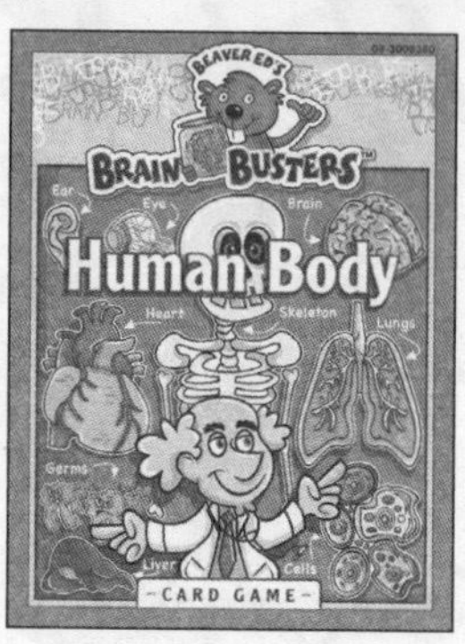

(All products by Beaver Books are available in English, French and Spanish)

Check out our website for more of our products:

www.beaverbooks.ca